SCAN THIS KEY
WITH YOUR MOBILE APP
TO UNLOCK THE BOOK

DON'T HAVE THE APP?

Download your app at:
incredebooks.com /disney

ISBN 978-0-993766-96-1

Olaf Wants A Birthday ©2015 Mercury InPress. All rights reserved.
© 2015 Disney Enterprises, Inc. All rights reserved.

Published by Mercury InPress Inc.
53 Auriga Drive, Ottawa, ON, Canada K2E 8C3

For additional information and permissions, please contact Mercury InPress Inc.

www.mercuryinpress.com

PRINTED IN CANADA

TURN TO LAST PAGE
FOR INSTRUCTIONS

OLAF WANTS A BIRTHDAY

An Interactive Rhyming Story For New Readers

By J.D. Franes

Illustrated by The Disney Storybook Art Team

What is a birthday?

I don't really know.

I'm only a snowman,

Just a few balls of snow.

Elsa built Anna

Playscapes with ice.

Those made on her birthday

Were especially nice.

Now having a birthday

Seems like such fun.

But what can I do

To celebrate one?

I want to spend time
With a wonderful friend.
A walk in the woods,
With my good buddy, Sven.

Wouldn't music be nice?

How about a song?

Something quite happy

That's not very long.

Are beach birthdays good?

Nothing's better, I think,

Than sun, surf, and seagulls,

And sand in my drink.

I want to see friends,
And if it isn't too late,
Let's freeze up the floor
And go for a skate.

I love playing games.

"Catch the snowman" is fun.

Marshmallow won't get me,

Because I really can run.

Anna loves cookies.

She calls them a treat.

Birthday cookies for me!

Would you like some to eat?

I'll pick wildflowers.

I'll choose them with care.

I'll pick just enough,

So we can all share.

I'm very excited,

And I'm happy to say,

I like birthdays so much,

I'll have one each day!

THE END

INSTRUCTIONS

DOWNLOAD

READ

PLAY

Get your Apple or
Android mobile app from
incredebooks.com/disney

Look for symbols in the
bottom corners of special
book pages.

Scan the special page
with your mobile app and
bring it to life in 3D.

Hold your mobile device over
special book pages to activate them.

For more information visit **incredebooks.com**

Incredebooks!™